This book belongs to

Name: _____

Cover Design by :
MATH-KNOTS LLC

First Edition :
December, 2019

Author:
Gowri Vemuri

Questions: mathknots.help@gmail.com

This book is dedicated to:

My Mom, who is my best critic, guide and supporter.

To what I am today, and what I am going to become tomorrow,

is all because of your blessings, unconditional affection and support.

This book is dedicated to the

strongest women of my life,

my dearest mom

and

to all those moms in this universe.

G.V.

What is NNAT ?

The Naglieri Nonverbal Ability Test (NNAT) is a group nonverbal ability test. These tests serve as a measure for identifying and placing students of K-12 for gifted and talented or Advanced Academic programs in many schools across USA.

The NNAT test is based on complex geometric shapes and figures to evaluate problem-solving and reasoning abilities of a child.

The test doesn't require mastery of any language, quantitative aptitude and Reading skills and uses minimum directions to solve the questions. The test measures the advanced levels of reasoning abilities of the child.

There are 4 types of questions on the NNAT test:

Pattern completion: Students Identify the missing portion of the given picture.

Reasoning by analogy: Relationship between the abstract geometric shapes is identified

Serial reasoning: A sequence of shapes, objects are identified

Example: the pattern is 1 ,2,3 then next row is either 3 , 2, 1 or 2, 3, 1 and the third row is 2, 3, 1 or 3 , 2, 1 based on second row choice.

NOTE: NO two rows will have the same pattern

What is NNAT ?

Spatial visualization: Two or more objects are combined to form a new object

Level	Grade	Pattern Completion	Analogy	Serial Reasoning	Spatial Visualization	Total
A	K	30	8			38
B	1	19	13	6		38
C	2	10	12	11	5	38
D	3-4	6	10	8	14	38
E	5-6	5	6	8	19	38
F	7-9	2	10	8	18	38
G	10-12		7	7	24	38

www.math-knots.com

Start from the middle of right choice and fully fill the bubble completely.

Wrong

A   B ◯   C ◯   D ◯

Wrong

A ◯   B ◯   C   D ◯

Wrong

A ◯   B ◯   C   D ◯

Partial Filled Bubble is not correct.

Correct

A ◯   B ◯   C ⬤   D ◯

PREPARATION FOR THE TEST

1. To simulate the testing format, a parent or an adult shall read the questions to the student to answer the practice test sets.

2. Student need to have a pencil and an eraser.

3. Student need to make sure they are bubbling the circles in the right way.

Before the testing date.

1. Make sure the child has a good nights sleep and a good breakfast.

www.math-knots.com

www.math-knots.com

TEST - 3

PATTERN COMPLETION

Ask the student to identify the missing portion of the given figure.
Bubble the right option A or B or C or D

Lets Start the Test...

1)

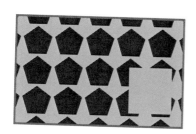

(A) ○

(B) ○

(C) ○

(D) ○

2)

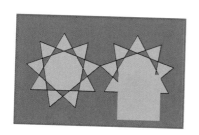

(A) ○

(B) ○

(C) ○

(D) ○

www.math-knots.com

3)

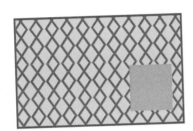

(A) ○   (B) ○   (C) ○   (D) ○

4)

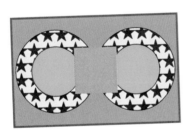

(A) ○   (B) ○   (C) ○   (D) ○

5)

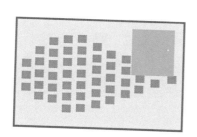

(A) ○

(B) ○

(C) ○

(D) ○

6)

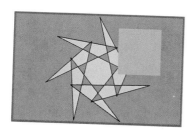

(A) ○

(B) ○

(C) ○

(D) ○

www.math-knots.com

7)

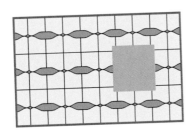

(A) ○   (B) ○   (C) ○   (D) ○

8)

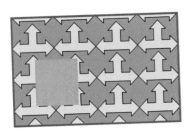

(A) ○   (B) ○   (C) ○   (D) ○

www.math-knots.com

9)

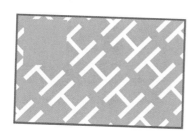

(A) ○

(B) ○

(C) ○

(D) ○

10)

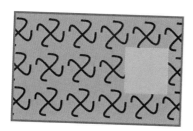

(A) ○

(B) ○

(C) ○

(D) ○

www.math-knots.com

11)

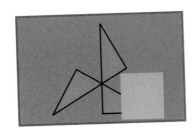

(A) ○

(B) ○

(C) ○

(D) ○

12)

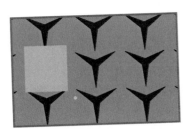

(A) ○

(B) ○

(C) ○

(D) ○

www.math-knots.com

13)

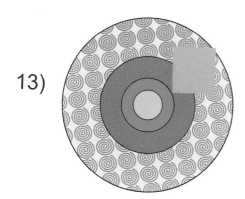

(A) ○   (B) ○   (C) ○   (D) ○

14)

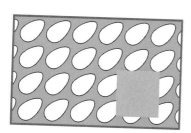

(A) ○   (B) ○   (C) ○   (D) ○

www.math-knots.com

15)

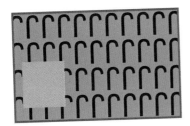

(A) ◯

(B) ◯

(C) ◯

(D) ◯

16)

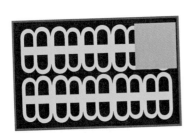

(A) ◯

(B) ◯

(C) ◯

(D) ◯

www.math-knots.com

TEST - 3

REASON BY ANALOGY

Ask the student to identify the relationship between the abstract geometric shapes given in the first row based on the same relationship identify the missing figure in the second row. Bubble the right option A or B or C or D

Lets Start the Test...

1)

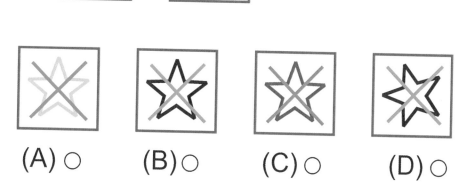

(A) ○   (B) ○   (C) ○   (D) ○

2)

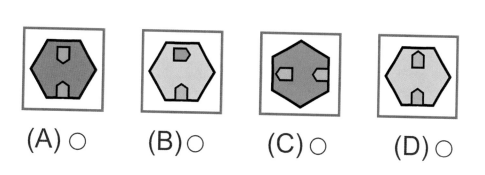

(A) ○   (B) ○   (C) ○   (D) ○

www.math-knots.com

3)

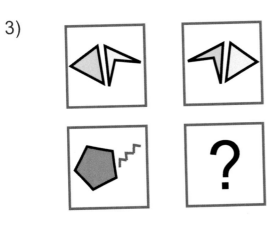

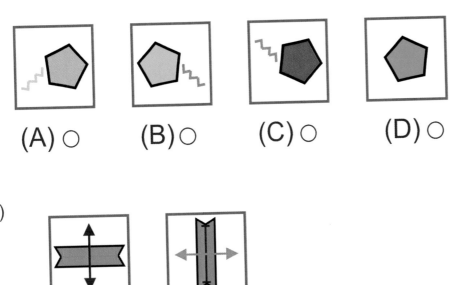

(A) ○   (B) ○   (C) ○   (D) ○

4)

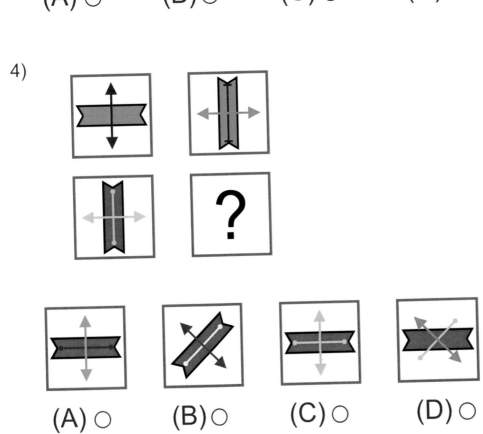

(A) ○   (B) ○   (C) ○   (D) ○

www.math-knots.com

5)

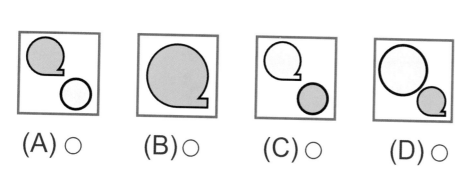

(A) ○   (B) ○   (C) ○   (D) ○

6)

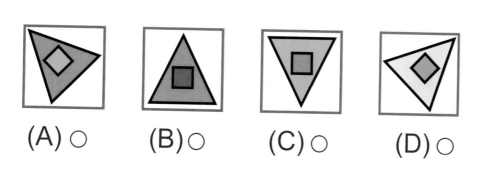

(A) ○   (B) ○   (C) ○   (D) ○

www.math-knots.com

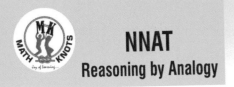
7)

(A) ○   (B) ○   (C) ○   (D) ○

8)

(A) ○   (B) ○   (C) ○   (D) ○

 www.math-knots.com

9)

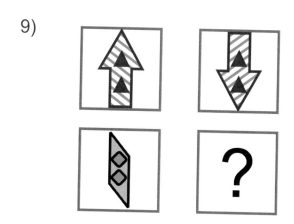

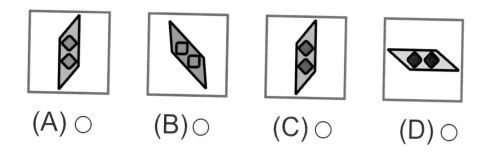

(A) ○   (B) ○   (C) ○   (D) ○

10)

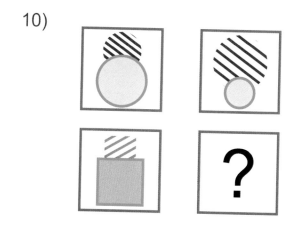

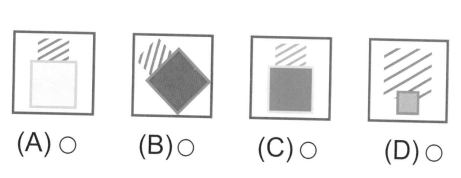

(A) ○   (B) ○   (C) ○   (D) ○

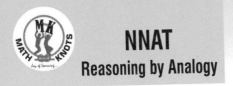
11)

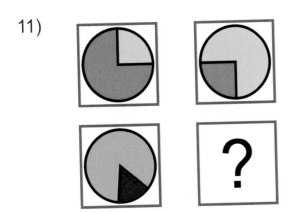

(A) ○　　(B) ○　　(C) ○　　(D) ○

12)

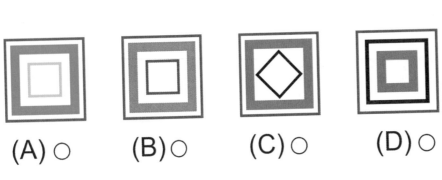

(A) ○　　(B) ○　　(C) ○　　(D) ○

13)

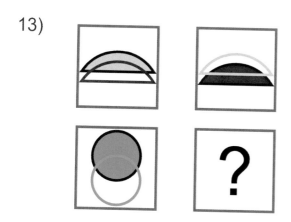

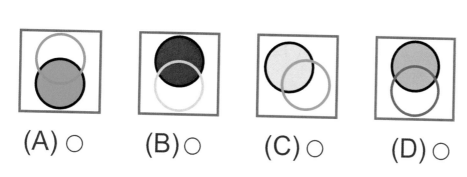

(A) ○   (B) ○   (C) ○   (D) ○

14)

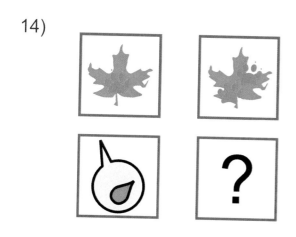

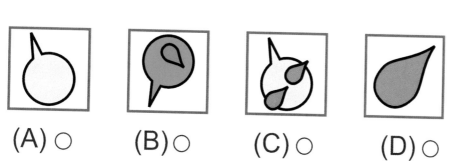

(A) ○   (B) ○   (C) ○   (D) ○

www.math-knots.com

15)

 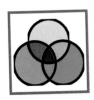

?

(A) ○   (B) ○   (C) ○   (D) ○

www.math-knots.com

TEST - 3

SERIAL REASONING

Ask the student to identify
the sequence of shapes or
objects and find the missing
figure in the matrix
Bubble the right option
A or B or C or D

Lets Start the Test...

1)

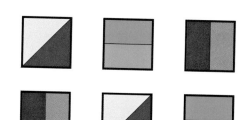

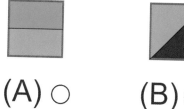 

(A) ○   (B) ○   (C) ○   (D) ○

2)

(A) ○   (B) ○   (C) ○   (D) ○

www.math-knots.com

3)

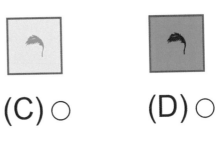

(A) ○   (B) ○   (C) ○   (D) ○

4)

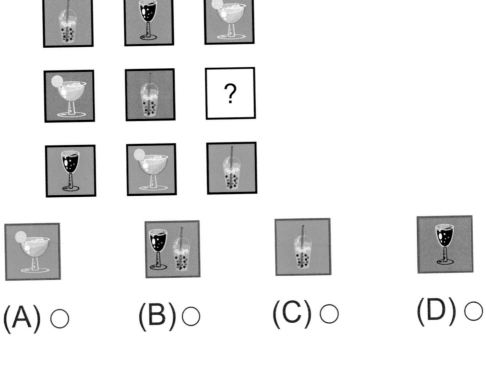

(A) ○   (B) ○   (C) ○   (D) ○

www.math-knots.com

5)

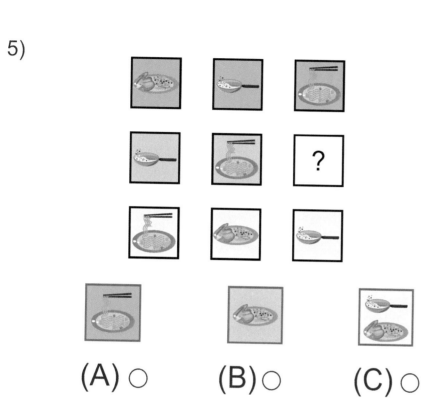

(A) ○   (B) ○   (C) ○   (D) ○

6)

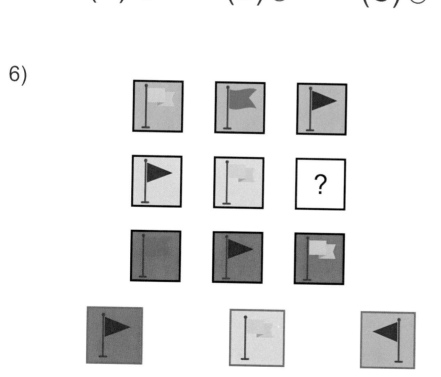

(A) ○   (B) ○   (C) ○   (D) ○

7)

?

(A) ○   (B) ○   (C) ○   (D) ○

8)

?

(A) ○   (B) ○   (C) ○   (D) ○

www.math-knots.com

9)

(A) ○   (B) ○   (C) ○   (D) ○

10)

(A) ○   (B) ○   (C) ○   (D) ○

11)

(A) ○   (B) ○   (C) ○   (D) ○

12)

(A) ○   (B) ○   (C) ○   (D) ○

13)

(A) ○   (B) ○   (C) ○   (D) ○

14)

(A) ○   (B) ○   (C) ○   (D) ○

www.math-knots.com

15)

(A) ○ (B) ○ (C) ○ (D) ○

16)

 ?

(A) ○ (B) ○ (C) ○ (D) ○

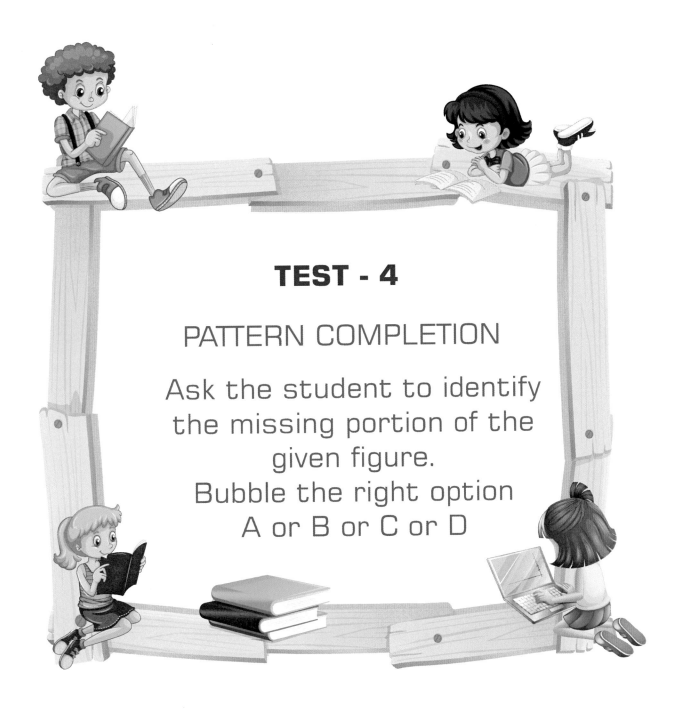

TEST - 4

PATTERN COMPLETION

Ask the student to identify
the missing portion of the
given figure.
Bubble the right option
A or B or C or D

Lets Start the Test...

www.math-knots.com

1)

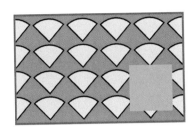

(A) ○

(B) ○

(C) ○

(D) ○

2)

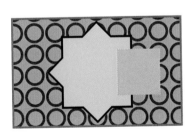

(A) ○

(B) ○

(C) ○

(D) ○

www.math-knots.com

3)

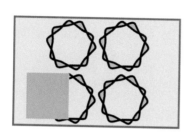

(A) ○

(B) ○

(C) ○

(D) ○

4)

(A) ○

(B) ○

(C) ○

(D) ○

www.math-knots.com

5)

(A) ○   (B) ○   (C) ○   (D) ○

6)

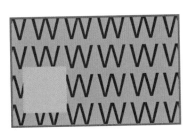

(A) ○   (B) ○   (C) ○   (D) ○

www.math-knots.com

7)

(A) ○

(B) ○

(C) ○

(D) ○

8)

(A) ○

(B) ○

(C) ○

(D) ○

www.math-knots.com

9)

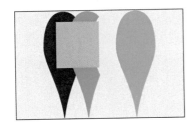

(A) ○

(B) ○

(C) ○

(D) ○

10)

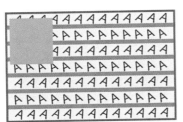

(A) ○

(B) ○

(C) ○

(D) ○

11)

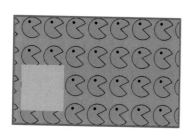

  (A) ○

  (B) ○

  (C) ○

  (D) ○

12)

  (A) ○

  (B) ○

  (C) ○

  (D) ○

www.math-knots.com

13)

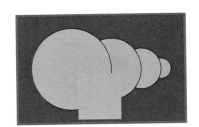

(A) ○

(B) ○

(C) ○

(D) ○

14)

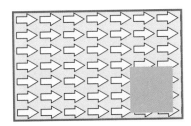

(A) ○

(B) ○

(C) ○

(D) ○

www.math-knots.com

15)

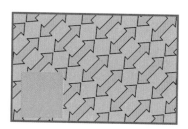

(A) ○   (B) ○   (C) ○   (D) ○

16)

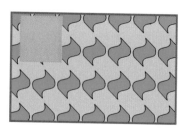

(A) ○   (B) ○   (C) ○   (D) ○

www.math-knots.com

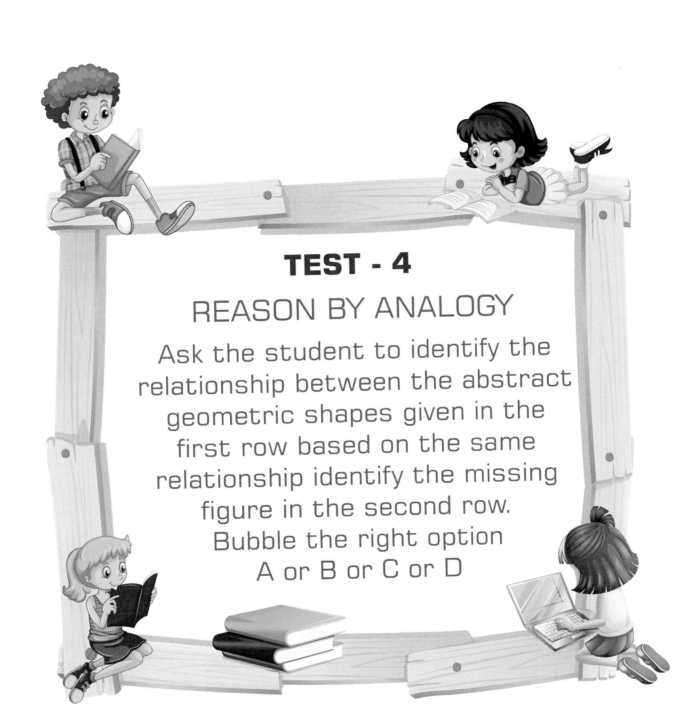

TEST - 4

REASON BY ANALOGY

Ask the student to identify the relationship between the abstract geometric shapes given in the first row based on the same relationship identify the missing figure in the second row. Bubble the right option A or B or C or D

Lets Start the Test...

www.math-knots.com

1)

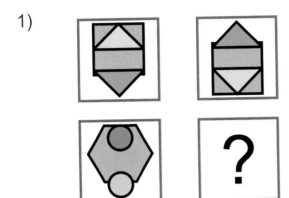

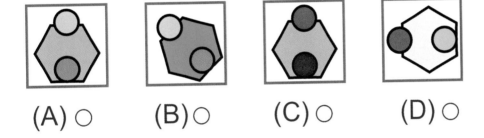

(A) ○   (B) ○   (C) ○   (D) ○

2)

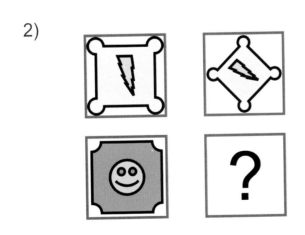

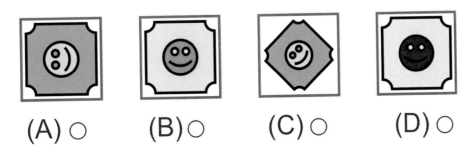

(A) ○   (B) ○   (C) ○   (D) ○

www.math-knots.com

3)

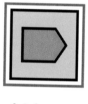   

(A) ○   (B) ○   (C) ○   (D) ○

4)

(A) ○   (B) ○   (C) ○   (D) ○

www.math-knots.com

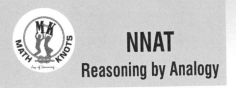
5)

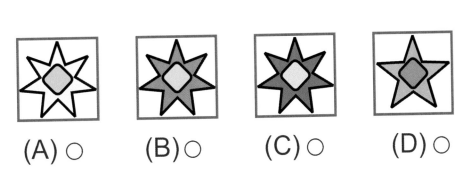

(A) ○   (B) ○   (C) ○   (D) ○

6)

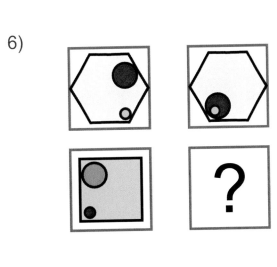

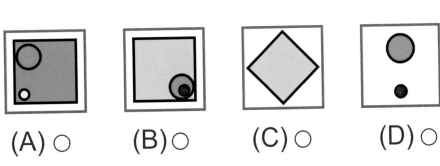

(A) ○   (B) ○   (C) ○   (D) ○

www.math-knots.com

7)

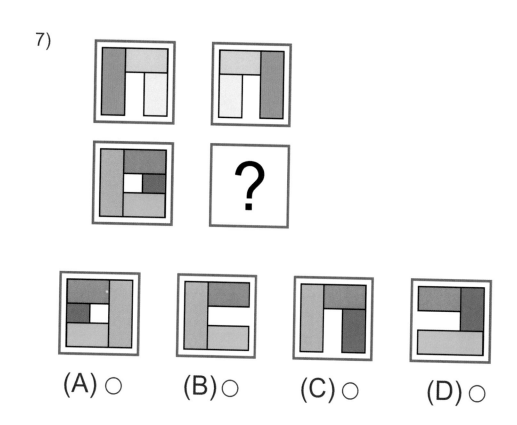

(A) ○   (B) ○   (C) ○   (D) ○

8)

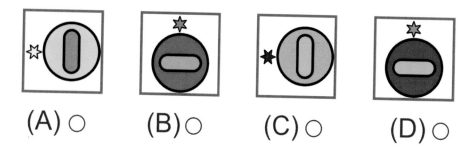

(A) ○   (B) ○   (C) ○   (D) ○

www.math-knots.com

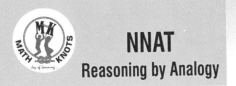

9)

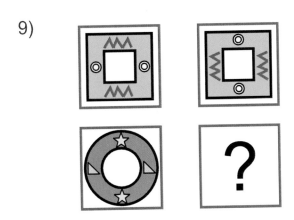

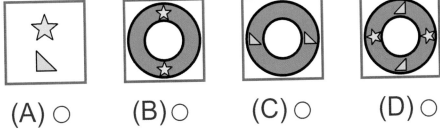

(A) ○   (B) ○   (C) ○   (D) ○

10)

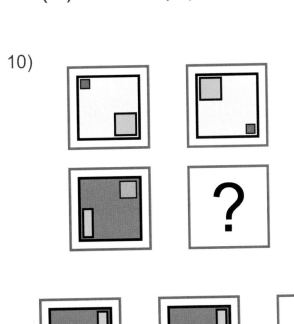

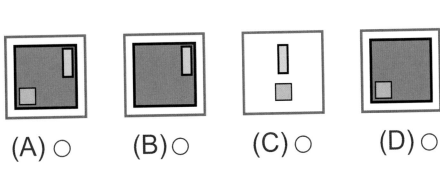

(A) ○   (B) ○   (C) ○   (D) ○

www.math-knots.com

11)

 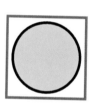

(A) ○　　(B) ○　　(C) ○　　(D) ○

12)

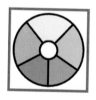 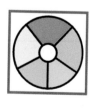 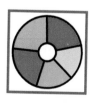 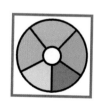

(A) ○　　(B) ○　　(C) ○　　(D) ○

13)

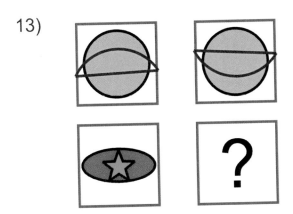

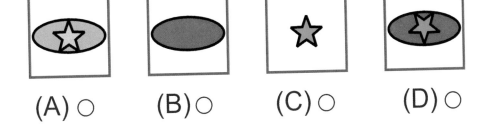

(A) ○   (B) ○   (C) ○   (D) ○

14)

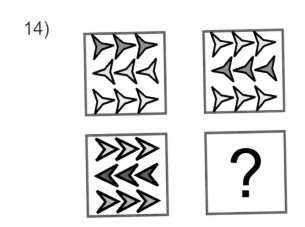

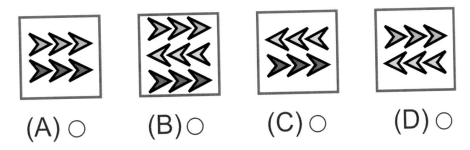

(A) ○   (B) ○   (C) ○   (D) ○

15)

 ?

(A) ○   (B) ○   (C) ○   (D) ○

www.math-knots.com

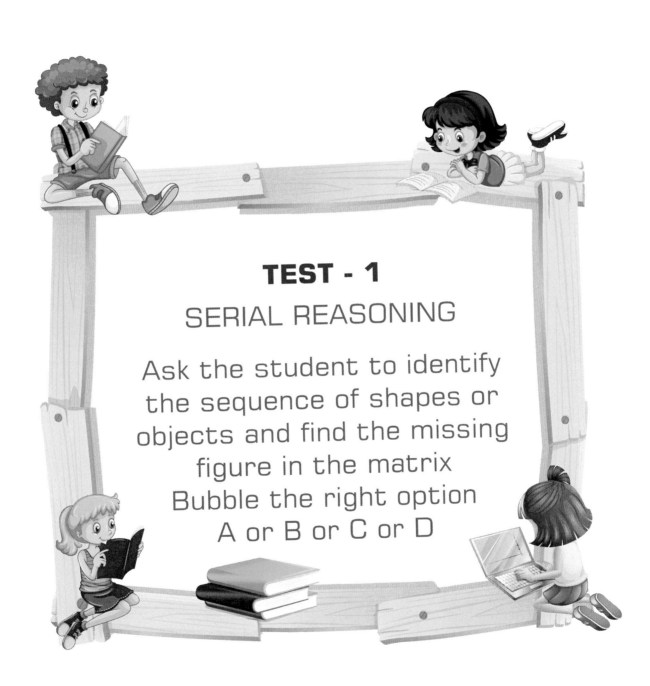

TEST - 1

SERIAL REASONING

Ask the student to identify
the sequence of shapes or
objects and find the missing
figure in the matrix
Bubble the right option
A or B or C or D

Lets Start the Test...

www.math-knots.com

1)

(A) ○   (B) ○   (C) ○   (D) ○

2)

(A) ○   (B) ○   (C) ○   (D) ○

3)

(A) ○　　(B) ○　　(C) ○　　(D) ○

4)

(A) ○　　(B) ○　　(C) ○　　(D) ○

www.math-knots.com

5)

(A) ○　　　(B) ○　　　(C) ○　　　(D) ○

6)

(A) ○　　　(B) ○　　　(C) ○　　　(D) ○

7)

(A) ○   (B) ○   (C) ○   (D) ○

8)

(A) ○   (B) ○   (C) ○   (D) ○

www.math-knots.com

9)

(A) ◯   (B) ◯   (C) ◯   (D) ◯

10)

(A) ◯   (B) ◯   (C) ◯   (D) ◯

11)

 ?

(A) ○   (B) ○   (C) ○   (D) ○

12)

?

(A) ○   (B) ○   (C) ○   (D) ○

www.math-knots.com

13)

(A) ○

(B) ○

(C) ○

(D) ○

14)

(A) ○

(B) ○

(C) ○

(D) ○

www.math-knots.com

15)

(A) ○   (B) ○   (C) ○   (D) ○

16)

(A) ○   (B) ○   (C) ○   (D) ○

www.math-knots.com

TEST 1 - 2 - 3

ANSWER KEYS

Lets Start the Test...

www.math-knots.com

Test 3 Answer Key

1. A

5. A

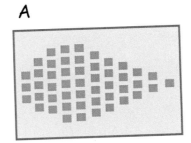

2. C

6. C

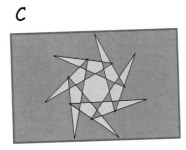

3. B

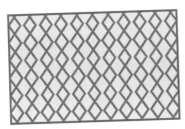

7. B

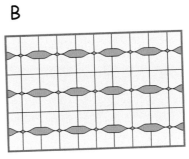

4. A

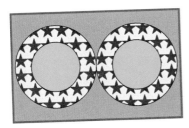

8. A

www.math-knots.com

Test 3 Answer Key

9. D

10. C

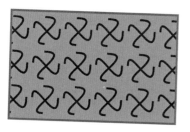

11. B

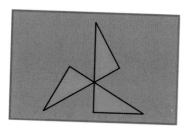

12. A

13. D

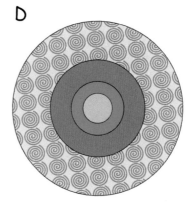

14. B

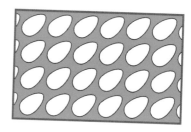

15. D

16. A

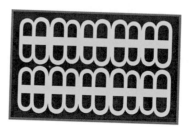

www.math-knots.com

Test 4 Answer Key

1. D

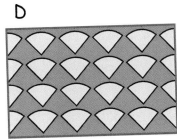

2. A

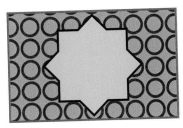

3. A

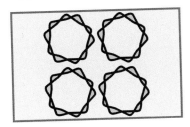

4. C

5. D

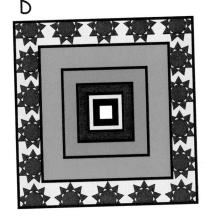

6. B

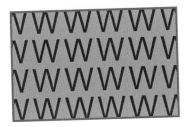

7. C

8. B

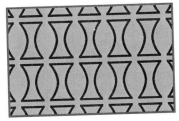

www.math-knots.com

Test 4 Answer Key

9. A

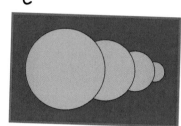

13. C

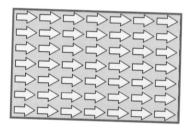

10. C

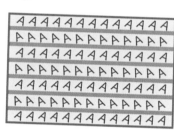

14. D

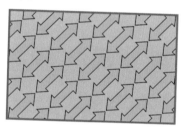

11. D

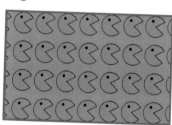

15. A

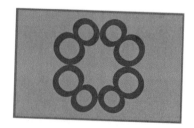

12. A

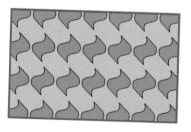

16. C

www.math-knots.com

Test 3

1. B
2. D
3. C
4. C
5. D
6. A
7. A
8. B
9. A
10. D
11. C
12. D
13. A
14. C
15. B

Test 4

1. A
2. C
3. C
4. A
5. D
6. B
7. A
8. C
9. D
10. A
11. C
12. A
13. D
14. B
15. A

www.math-knots.com

Test 3		Test 4	
1.	A	1.	A
2.	B	2.	A
3.	D	3.	C
4.	D	4.	B
5.	B	5.	A
6.	D	6.	D
7.	C	7.	C
8.	A	8.	A
9.	B	9.	C
10.	A	10.	D
11.	D	11.	B
12.	A	12.	C
13.	D	13.	C
14.	B	14.	A
15.	D	15.	D
16.	A	16.	C

www.math-knots.com

www.math-knots.com

Made in the USA
Middletown, DE
04 October 2023

40213754R00046